DOCTOR·WHO

BBC CHILDREN'S BOOKS
Published by the Penguin Group
Penguin Books Ltd, 80 Strand, London, WC2R 0RL, England
Penguin Group (USA) Inc., 375 Hudson Street, New York, New York 10014, USA
Penguin Books (Australia) Ltd, 250 Camberwell Road, Camberwell, Victoria 3124, Australia.
(A division of Pearson Australia Group Pty Ltd)
Canada, India, New Zealand, South Africa
Published by BBC Children's Books, 2008
Text and design © Children's Character Books, 2008
Written by Stephen Cole
10 9 8 7 6 5 4 3 2 1
ISBN-13: 978-1-40590-445-2
Printed in Great Britain by Clays Ltd, St Ives plc

DOCTOR · WHO

QUIZ BOOK 4

CONTENTS

WHEN DOCTORS MEET

Following a near-disastrous collision in the vortex, the Doctor — much to his delight — found himself face-to-familiar-face with one of his earlier selves! To kick off this quiz book, see if you can remember what happened...

1. What was the nature of the Time Crash?

a) The TARDIS had run aground on the Dark Matter Reefs.

b) The TARDIS had hit an asteroid filled with pockets of raw time travel fuel.

c) The TARDIS had collided with an earlier version of itself.

2. How is the Fifth Doctor dressed?

a) In stripy pyjamas.

b) In old-fashioned cricketing gear.

c) In a dark suit and tie.

3. Why did the Fifth Doctor's appearance seem slightly different?

a) Because of time spillage from the TARDIS console.

b) Because of the time differential of having two Doctors in the same place at the same time.

c) Because the memory cheats.

4. The Fifth Doctor thinks his older self is:

a) A fan.

b) The Master.

c) Tegan.

5. The paradox of the TARDIS crashing into itself threatens to punch a hole in the universe the size of:

a) Earth.

b) Wales.

c) Belgium.

6. The crash was made possible because:

a) The Tenth Doctor wanted to play bumper cars.

b) The Fifth Doctor's TARDIS was sabotaged by Cybermen.

c) The Tenth Doctor forgot to activate the defence shields of his TARDIS when rebuilding it.

7. How did the Doctors resolve the situation?

a) By reconfiguring their two TARDISes into time-cone inverters.

b) By jettisoning fifty percent of the TARDIS interior.

c) By creating a supernova to balance out the black hole caused by the collision.

8. How did the Tenth Doctor know how to put right the paradox and restore stability to the universe?

a) He's very clever.

b) He remembered watching himself do it, back when he was the Fifth Doctor.

c) It was blind luck.

9. What did the Fifth Doctor almost leave behind on the TARDIS console?

a) His coat.

b) His hat.

c) His trainers.

10. What were the Fifth Doctor's final words of advice to his future self before fading away?

a) 'Remember to put your shields up...'

b) 'Eat more celery!'

c) 'Watch out for the Daleks!'

A RHYMING RIDDLE

Study the riddle below, written by one of the Doctor's adversaries. Each line gives you the clue to a particular letter. If you guess all the right letters and spell them out in order you will get the name of these robotic killers!

Our first is in HEAVEN but also in HELL,

Our second's in HALO and also HOTEL,

Our third is in CHRISTMAS and also in SING,

Our fourth's in TITANIC — such dangers we bring!

We look like kind angels of glittering gold,

But stay well away if you wish to grow old!

VOYAGE OF THE DAMNED

TRUE OR FALSE?

It seems unlikely that the Doctor will ever enjoy a peaceful Christmas, but recently his struggles against evil were even more *Titanic* than usual! Were you sharing his festive struggles, or too busy scoffing turkey to notice? See if you can say whether the statements below are true or false.

1. The TARDIS landed on top of the *Titanic*'s funnel.
   TRUE/FALSE

2. This particular *Titanic* was an interstellar pleasure cruiser. *TRUE/FALSE*

3. The Doctor became friends with a waitress called Astrid. *TRUE/FALSE*

4. The Captain of the *Titanic* tried to stop his midshipman from sabotaging the vessel. *TRUE/FALSE*

5. The badly damaged *Titanic* ended up on a collision course with Mars. *TRUE/FALSE*

6. The Doctor, Astrid and the other survivors were helped to safety by robotic angels called the Host. *TRUE/FALSE*

7. The Host were working for former cruise line owner Max Capricorn, a bitter, cybernetic creature. *TRUE/FALSE*

8. Astrid crashed into Capricorn with a forklift truck and the two of them plunged over a precipice. *TRUE/FALSE*

9. The Doctor could not stop the out-of-control *Titanic* from crashing. *TRUE/FALSE*

10. Astrid joined the Doctor for further adventures in the TARDIS. *TRUE/FALSE*

ANSWERS:
1. False, 2. True, 3. True, 4. False, 5. False, 6. False, 7. True, 8. True, 9. False, 10. False.

SCORES:
8-10 A truly *Titanic* score and one to be proud of!

5-7 Did someone sneakily sabotage your head while you were watching?

0-4 A Host of wrong answers makes this a far from heavenly score. Looks like the Christmas pudding was YOU!

A NOBLE COMPANION

When Donna first met the Doctor, she turned down the chance to travel with him. But she soon regretted that mistake! Have you been following her incredible journey as she travelled at the Doctor's side? If so, you'll find this quiz a Donna-doddle...

1. What is the name of Donna's mum?

a) Brenda.

b) Sylvia.

c) Jackie.

2. What was Donna's occupation before she joined the Doctor?

a) Temp/office worker.

b) Fitness instructor.

c) Chef.

3. Where was Donna when the Cybermen and Daleks battled over Canary Wharf in London?

a) Helping to evacuate survivors.

b) Scuba diving.

c) Running a soup kitchen for homeless victims.

4. What was Donna doing shortly before she first met the Doctor?

a) Getting married.

b) Bungee jumping.

c) Photocopying secret documents.

5. The first alien Donna encountered was:

a) A Judoon.

b) An Adipose.

c) The Empress of the Racnoss.

6. What is the name of Donna's granddad?

a) Wilfred Mott.

b) John Jones.

c) Walter Noble.

7. Where did Donna go on her first journey into the past?

a) The coronation of Queen Victoria.

b) Pompeii in AD79.

c) 4.6 billion years ago to the creation of Earth.

8. Which aliens did Donna meet on her first visit to another world?

a) The Adipose.

b) The Ood.

c) The Hath.

9. On the planet Messaline, what natural talent of Donna's came in particularly useful?

a) Her skill with numbering systems.

b) Her cooking ability.

c) Her knack for impersonating musical instruments.

10. Why did the Doctor part company with Donna?

a) They had a row.

b) The Doctor was forced to wipe her mind of everything they ever did together in order to save her life.

c) Donna got bored of travelling in the TARDIS.

SCORES:

7-10 When it comes to knowing Donna, you are the DON!

4-6 Donna's mum would give you one of her famous lectures if she knew you'd got so many questions wrong!

0-3 What an *ignoble* result! Pay more attention next time — you don't know what you're missing!

ANSWERS:

1.b, 2.a, 3.b, 4.a, 5.c, 6.a, 7.c, 8.b, 9.a, 10.b.

PARTNERS IN CRIME

TRUE OR FALSE?

The Doctor and Donna's destinies were bound up in ways neither of them could suspect… and their adventure with Miss Foster and the Adipose saw them reunited after their first encounter. But how much do you recall about their action-packed reunion?

1. Donna and the Doctor were both investigating Adipose Industries. *TRUE/FALSE*

2. They met straight away in a busy office. *TRUE/FALSE*

3. The diet pills sold by Adipose Industries were alien in origin. *TRUE/FALSE*

4. People who took the pills transformed into giant Adipose creatures. *TRUE/FALSE*

5. The person behind the Adipose scheme was Miss Foster. *TRUE/FALSE*

6. She was planning to use the Adipose to wipe out the entire human race. *TRUE/FALSE*

7. The Doctor and Donna escaped down the side of a building in a window cleaner's cradle. *TRUE/FALSE*

8. Several thousand Adipose made their way across London to the Adipose Industries building. *TRUE/FALSE*

9. They were transported away from Earth in an invisible proton sphere. *TRUE/FALSE*

10. At the end of the adventure, Donna decided to remain on Earth. *TRUE/FALSE*

ANSWERS:

1. True. 2. False. 3. True. 4. False. 5. True. 6. True. 7. False. 8. True. 9. False. 10. False.

SCORES:

8-10 Your brain is a lean, mean thinking machine — well done!

4-7 Not a bad score, but you perhaps need a little help digesting Doctor Who stories...

0-3 You want to be a *Doctor Who* expert? FAT chance!

THE MONSTER'S RIDDLE

Study the riddle below. Each line gives you the clue to a particular letter. If you guess all the right letters and spell them out in order you will get the name of one of the more unusual aliens in the Doctor's universe.

My first is in ALIEN, also in AWE,

My second's in DINKY, that's me for sure!

My third is in CHILD and in LITTLE as well,

My fourth is in PERIL but never in SWELL,

My fifth is in BLOBBY and also OBESE,

My sixth is in SQUEEZE as our numbers increase!

My seventh's in TEETH though
I've just got the one,

Now I'm off to meet
up with my parents
— they've WON!

ODD ONE OUT

Look at the different groups of people, places and things below. In each case, which is the odd one out – and why?

1. Solana Mercurio, Chief Executive Halpen, Harriet Jones, Dr Ryder.

2. Pyrovillia, the Lost Moon of Poosh, Earth, Messaline, Clom.

3. Spartacus, John Smith, Chief Inspector Smith, Doctor Moon.

4. Cliffs of Oblivion, Mount Vesuvius, the Multi-Faceted Coast, Winter Witch Canyon.

5. Jenny, Sarah Jane Smith, Captain Jack, Martha Jones.

6. Skorr, Staal, Sanchez.

ANSWERS:

1. Harriet Jones — the others work for Ood Operations.

2. Messaline — the other worlds were among those taken out of time and space by the Daleks.

3. Doctor Moon — the others are all false identities the Doctor has used.

4. Mount Vesuvius — the others are geographical features found on the planet Midnight.

5. Jenny — the others joined the Doctor fighting Davros and the Daleks.

6. Sanchez — he is a human soldier, while the others are all Sontarans.

SCORES:

5-6   Superb reasoning. You could join the Rattigan Academy!

3-4   Your mind is fairly sharp — with hard work and dedication you might just join the Rattigan Academy.

1-2   You could maybe join the Rattigan Academy cleaning the toilets.

0   What's an academy?

VILE VILLAINS!

The Doctor is always running into monsters, but sometimes the most horrible creatures come in human form... How much do you know about the latest lot of humanoid baddies he's come up against?

1. By which name was Matron Cofelia of the Five-Straighten Classabindi Nursery Fleet, Intergalactic Class known on Earth?

a) Miss Demeanour.

b) Miss Isle.

c) Miss Foster.

2. Which alien power possessed Lucius Petrus Dextrus in first century Pompeii?

a) The Pyrovile.

b) The Hath.

c) The Sontarans.

3. Which part of Lucius Petrus Dextrus had been turned to stone?

a) His leg.

b) His head.

c) His right arm.

4. What is the full name of the Chief Executive of Ood Operations?

a) Dalek Caan.

b) Klineman Halpen.

c) Solana Mercurio.

5. What did child genius Luke Rattigan invent when he was just 12 years old?

a) The Fountain Six Search Engine.

b) The Omega Pulse Engine.

c) The ATMOS system.

6. Who was in charge of the human forces on Messaline?

a) Colonel Bobb.

b) General Cobb.

c) Major Flob.

7. What human identity did the Vespiform take?

a) Reverend Golightly.

b) Agatha Christie.

c) Lady Eddison.

8. What did Guard Commander Kess use to catch and almost kill the Doctor in a warehouse on the Ood-Sphere?

a) A floating pain-balloon.

b) A radio-controlled rocket.

c) A giant metal lifting claw.

BIG UNIVERSE

For the Doctor and his companions, the whole universe is their playground. There are infinite worlds and countless wonders awaiting the Doctor and his friends in the cosmos — but how much can you remember about some of those we've already been shown or told about? Take the quiz and find out...

1. What is the name of the Sontarans' home planet?

a) Sontar.

b) Sontarask Prime.

c) Cloneworld Alpha.

2. The Ood–Sphere is in the same solar system as which other planet?

a) Oodos Minor.

b) Earth.

c) The Sense-Sphere.

3. The inhabitants of the planet Pyrovillia were:

a) Creatures of fire and rock.

b) Creatures of smoke.

c) Creatures of sticky tar.

4. What is the name of the 'lost' Adipose breeding planet?

a) Adipose Three.

b) Antrobus.

c) Fataria.

5. Far out beyond Alpha Geminorum lies a planet designated Castor-36. Why is it of interest to genius schemer Luke Rattigan?

a) He plans to lead a party of geniuses to colonise it.

b) He wants to lead the Sontarans there to conquer it.

c) He wants to dump Earth's pollution there.

6. Certain bees on Earth are extraterrestrial! These so-called 'Migrant Bees' hail from the planet:

a) Melissa Majoria.

b) Mephisto Hive One.

c) Tanana-Ree.

7. The intergalactic cruise liner *Titanic* came from which planet?

a) Earth.

b) Sto.

c) Starloss.

8. According to 'DoctorDonna', on the planet Felspoon you will find:

a) Towering Dalek sculptures.

b) Mountains that sway in the breeze.

c) Lakes that float in the air.

9. Where do the terrifying Vespiforms have their hives?

a) In the Condensate Wilderness.

b) In the Woods of Plinn.

c) In the Silfrax Galaxy.

10. What is the name of the Daleks' home planet?

a) Skaro.

b) Yarvelling.

c) Dallimus.

11. The planet Messaline was colonised by:

a) Humans and the Hath.

b) The Hath and the Hathnots.

c) The Sontarans.

12. Which area of the universe containing a rift in space–time was taken out of time by the Daleks?

a) The Blackland Starcoast.

b) The Medusa Cascade.

c) The Hiding Shroud.

13. On the Ood–Sphere, what was discovered under the Northern Glacier?

a) Oil.

b) The skeleton of a giant Ood.

c) An enormous brain.

14. The planet Midnight orbits which kind of star?

a) X-tonic.

b) Ultraviolet.

c) Red Giant.

15. What was the name of the gigantic space library encountered by the Doctor and Donna?

a) Biblios Three.

b) The Library.

c) Papperbok Bind.

16. On which planet did Donna reach her journey's end?

a) Skaro.

b) Woman Wept.

c) Earth.

THE FIRES OF POMPEII

TRUE OR FALSE?

The Doctor and Donna arrived in Pompeii in AD79 just as Mount Vesuvius was about to blow... but is your knowledge of those events white hot or just gently glowing? Find out by answering true or false to the following statements and checking your score below. *Veni, vidi, vici...!*

1. The Doctor took Donna to Pompeii to see Mount Vesuvius explode. *TRUE/FALSE*

2. Donna wanted to warn everyone in Pompeii that the volcano was about to erupt. *TRUE/FALSE*

3. The Doctor agreed with her. *TRUE/FALSE*

4. The TARDIS was stolen by alien beings. *TRUE/FALSE*

5. The Doctor discovered that the local soothsayers were under an alien influence that was slowly turning them to stone. *TRUE/FALSE*

6. A huge blazing hot stone creature menaced the Doctor. *TRUE/FALSE*

7. The Doctor and Donna discovered that aliens were trying to destroy humanity and take over the world. *TRUE/FALSE*

8. The Doctor destroyed all the aliens with a glass of water. *TRUE/FALSE*

9. The Doctor was able to stop Mount Vesuvius from erupting. *TRUE/FALSE*

10. Life in Pompeii went on happily. *TRUE/FALSE*

ANSWERS:
1. False. 2. True. 3. False. 4. False. 5. True 6. True. 7. True. 8. True. 9. False. 10. False.

SCORES:
8-10 Well done — the fires of Pompeii burn strongly in you.
5-7 Hmmm, if this is the best score you can manage you must be a bit burnt out.
0-4 Your brain cells seem to have gone up in smoke. Hopefully you'll have an eruption of fresh inspiration soon!

SONTARAN SENSE

They are short, squat and deadly, with designs upon Earth... That much is obvious. But how much do you really know about the sinister Sontaran race?

1. Why do Sontarans all look so similar?

a) They are identical twins born to the same mother.

b) They are a clone race.

c) They have plastic surgery so they all appear identical.

2. How many fingers does a Sontaran have?

a) Five.

b) Six.

c) Three.

3. What is the nickname of General Staal of the Tenth Sontaran Battle Fleet?

a) Staal the Undefeated.

b) Staal the Very Strong.

c) Good ole Staaly.

4. What is the only weak point of a Sontaran?

a) The antic opening.

b) The fourth eye.

c) The probic vent.

5. Where is this weak point located?

a) At the back of the neck.

b) At the back of the foot.

c) Below the left eye.

6. The Sontarans have been waging a lengthy interstellar war with which alien race?

a) The Daleks.

b) The Rutans.

c) The Cybermen.

7. What is the nickname of Commander Skorr of the Tenth Sontaran Battle Fleet?

a) Skorr, the blood-bringer.

b) Skorr, the all-time winner.

c) Skorr, the iron fisted warrior born.

8. What is the name of the Sontaran gas designed to change Earth's atmosphere?

a) Caesofine Concentrate.

b) Sontar Vapour.

c) Death Cell gas.

PLANET OF THE OOD

TRUE OR FALSE?

When they landed on the Ood-Sphere in 4126, the Doctor and Donna were soon caught up in a case of sinister exploitation and centuries-old revenge... How much do you remember of those brain-bursting events? Find out by taking the true-or-false test...

1. The Doctor deliberately took the TARDIS to the Ood-Sphere. *TRUE/FALSE*

2. The Ood were starting to turn savage and disobedient *TRUE/FALSE*

3. Their eyes turned bright yellow. *TRUE/FALSE*

4. Chief Executive Halpen, who made money from selling Ood treated them kindly and fairly. *TRUE/FALSE*

5. The Ood kept saying, 'The square must be broken.'
TRUE/FALSE

6. The Doctor discovered the Ood were born with secondary brains, cut off by Halpen's company and replaced with translators. *TRUE/FALSE*

7. Halpen tried to have all the rogue Ood destroyed.
TRUE/FALSE

8. Then Halpen turned into a large fish, and his company was no more. *TRUE/FALSE*

9. The free Ood sang joyfully to celebrate their freedom.
TRUE/FALSE

10. Donna stayed behind to help the Ood begin a new life.
TRUE/FALSE

ANSWERS:

1. False 2. True 3. False 4. False 5. False 6. True 7. True 8. False 9. True 10. False.

SCORES:

8-10 You are clearly a big Ood fan. Do you have a bald head and red tendrils hanging out of your mouth?

5-7 Not a fantastic score — why not study Solana Mercurio's files and swot up on your Ood facts?

0-4 Watch out for giant claws in the ceiling — they might be dunking down to take you away sometime soon!

38

FANTASTIC FATES!

The Doctor battles for life, but his adventures are often haunted by the spectre of death and disaster. And despite his best efforts, some people in this dangerous universe — whether fighting for good or for evil — come to an unpleasant or incredible end. Can you remember the last moments of the characters below?

1. Guard Commander Kess was:

a) Shot by the Daleks.

b) Shot by the Sontarans.

c) A victim of the same deadly gas he had released to wipe out the Ood.

2. Miss Foster fell:

a) From a window cleaner's cradle.

b) From a great height when her levitation beam was switched off.

c) For a Vespiform and was stung to death.

3. Miss Chandrakala was:

a) Crushed by a stone gargoyle.

b) Killed by jewel thief the Unicorn.

c) Banished to an alien dimension.

4. The Hostess on the planet Midnight:

a) Was shot by a Sontaran.

b) Sacrificed herself to destroy a sinister alien force.

c) Was poisoned by alien coffee.

5. The Donna Noble who never met the Doctor:

a) Threw herself in front of a lorry to put Earth's history back on track.

b) Lived happily ever after.

c) Was atomised in an experimental time machine.

6. Stacy Campbell, who took Adipose slimming pills:

a) Fell from a high window.

b) Had her entire body converted into Adipose young.

c) Fell down her own toilet.

7. Chief Executive Halpen of Ood Operations...

a) Was turned into an Ood himself.

b) Was cloned by the Sontarans.

c) Was blown up by his own bombs.

8. Harriet Jones, former
British Prime Minister...

a) Was killed by the Slitheen.

b) Published her autobiography
and was arrested by Torchwood.

c) Was killed by Daleks.

41

MONSTERS UNLEASHED

The most recent crop of monsters encountered by the Doctor has been among the most weird and wonderful yet. The next quiz will test you on how much MONSTROUS information you can remember...

1. What do the Hath have built into their faces?

a) Gas-masks.

b) Electro-goggles.

c) Translucent tubes of liquid.

2. When a Sontaran removes its helmet it is facing battle:

a) Openskinned.

b) Helmetless.

c) Face-favoured.

3. How many people were at risk from Miss Foster's attempt to convert them into Adipose?

a) One hundred.

b) One thousand.

c) One million.

4. What weapon did the Doctor use against the Pyrovile?

a) A heat-induction thermo-ray.

b) A laser spanner.

c) A water pistol.

5. Which race of tiny, carnivorous creatures infested the Library?

a) The Vashta Nerada.

b) The Nanobytes.

c) The Doom Dust.

6. What race of intergalactic law-enforcers help guard the headquarters of the Shadow Proclamation?

a) The Daleks.

b) The Sontarans.

c) The Judoon.

7. What did the robotic Host aboard the *Titanic* use to kill their victims?

a) Their halos.

b) Laser guns.

c) Detachable wings.

8. What is the technical term for the goo left behind when a Vespiform changes its physical form?

a) Ectoslime.

b) Morphic residue.

c) Gurgle-paste.

THE SONTARAN STRATAGEM

When an old enemy returned to menace the Doctor with a devious plan to change Earth forever, it looked like the end for the Doctor, his friends and civilisation as we know it! Could you bear to watch, or were you out panicking in the streets? Look at the statements below and see if you can tell what's true and what's false.

1. The Doctor was summoned to Earth by a call from his old friend Martha Jones. *TRUE/FALSE*

2. She wanted him to investigate alien technology that had been installed in millions of cars worldwide. *TRUE/FALSE*

3. The technology was supposed to remove harmful gases from the atmosphere. *TRUE/FALSE*

4. The technology was part of an evil Sontaran plan. *TRUE/FALSE*

5. The Sontarans were being helped by a human genius named Boris Brannigan. *TRUE/FALSE*

6. They made a clone of Donna to spy for them on Earth. *TRUE/FALSE*

7. The Sontarans used the technology in the cars to release toxic gases into the atmosphere. *TRUE/FALSE*

8. They planned to turn Earth into a holiday world for recovering Sontaran soldiers. *TRUE/FALSE*

9. The Doctor fought the Sontaran leader in hand-to-hand combat. *TRUE/FALSE*

10. The Sontarans retreated and promised never to return. *TRUE/FALSE*

ANSWERS:

1. True. 2. True. 3. True. 4. True. 5. False. 6. False. 7. True. 8. False. 9. False. 10. False.

SCORES:

8-10 Congratulations — when it comes to coming first, you're as single-minded as a Sontaran!

5-7 You're not the smartest in the Sontaran battle fleet, but perhaps if you done some of your brain cells you'll do better next time.

0-4 Did someone hit you on your probic vent before you started this quiz? Go and have a lie down!

QUESTIONS FOR ANSWERS

The following random quiz questions were teleported to the core of the book and suffered some transcription errors. In each case you'll find the correct answer has been given to you first — so now you must choose the question that would get you that answer...

1. Ood Sigma.

a) Who tried to breed Adipose out of human fat?

b) Who was Chief Executive Halpen's personal assistant?

c) Who tried to alter Earth's atmosphere with a deadly gas?

2. The Sibylline Sisterhood.

a) To which sect of female soothsayers was Evelina promised?

b) Who summoned the Doctor to the Library?

c) Who tried to steal the Firestone?

3. A magnatron.

a) What did the Doctor use to defeat the Sontarans?

b) What did the Daleks use to drag planets through space?

c) What did Cline use to generate a soldier from the Doctor's flesh?

4. 4022.

a) How many life forms in the Library were saved by its central hard disk?

b) How many Sontarans were poised to invade Earth?

c) How many Dalek saucers attacked Torchwood?

5. He was a Vespiform.

a) What was the secret of the man Lady Eddison fell in love with in 19th century India?

b) What was Mickey Smith's reason for wanting to leave the parallel dimension?

c) What made Professor Hobbes research the history of the planet Midnight?

6. 27.

a) How many fingers does a Sontaran have on one hand?

b) How many lives does the Doctor have?

c) How many planets did the Daleks pull out of time and space in order to operate their ultimate weapon?

ANSWERS (OR RATHER QUESTIONS):

1. b, 2. a, 3. b, 4. a, 5. a, 6. c.

SCORES:

5-6   Clearly you are not deterred by a change of form. You probably wouldn't blink if your best mate turned into a Vespiform before your eyes!

3-4   Perhaps your thoughts suffered a few transcription errors as they whizzed about your brain. Better luck next time.

0-2   The answer is 'LOSER'. What do you think the question might be?

KEY MOMENTS

Look at the scenes on the following pages and see if you can identify which of the Doctor's adventures they belong to.

ANSWERS

A. Planet of the Ood.

B. Forest of the Dead.

C. The Unicorn and the Wasp.

D. Voyage of the Damned.

E. The Stolen Earth

F. Partners in Crime.

G. Silence in the Library.

H. The Poison Sky.

I. The Sontaran Stratagem.

J. The Fires of Pompeii.

K. Journey's End.

L. The Doctor's Daughter.

WHAT IS *THAT*?!

One thing in the Doctor's universe is certain... Tantalising techno-jargon, baffling code names and effortlessly exotic explanations will be forever tripping off his Time Lord tongue — or the tongues of those around him! Extraordinary gadgets, unlikely inventions and far-out threats are the order of the day — but when it comes to understanding them, are you a Luke Rattigan or a Miss Evangelista? Test yourself and see!

1. What does ATMOS stand for?

a) A Terrible, Monstrous Operating System.

b) Atmospheric Omission System.

c) A Tin Machine On Skaro.

2. What is the purpose of a Progenation Machine?

a) It creates a new life form from a single living organism.

b) It prolongs generations.

c) It produces instant meals for armies on the move.

3. **What was the true function of the Firestone jewel?**

a) It gave the owner control over all wasps.

b) It could create fire from any stone.

c) It was a Vespiform telepathic recorder.

4. **What does UNIT stand for?**

a) United Ninjas In Trouble.

b) Unified Intelligence Taskforce.

c) Unidentified Nemesis Information Trust.

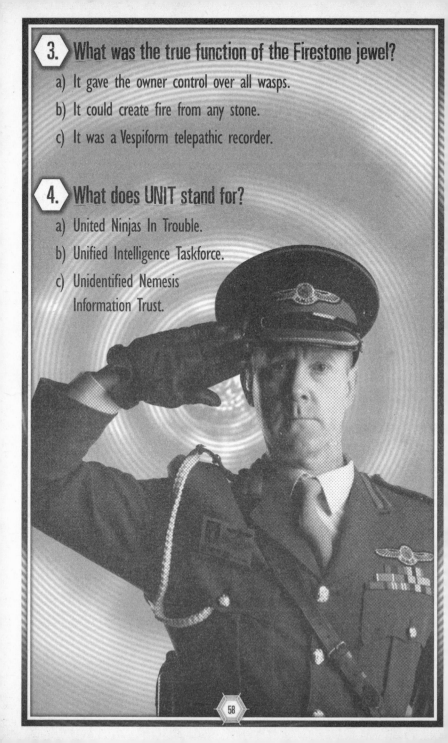

5. The Daleks caught the TARDIS in a chronon loop
— what's that?

a) A kind of temporal prison.

b) A device that ties loops in its victims' chronons.

c) A large, twisted metal shell made of looped molecules.

6. What is the Crusader 50?

a) A robotic knight for hire.

b) A rugged all-terrain exploration vehicle.

c) A make of fridge in the 51st century.

7. What was Operation Blue Sky?

a) The plan to make the surface of the planet Messaline habitable.

b) A raid on the ATMOS distribution centre by UNIT troops.

c) An operation to make Earth's sky permanently blue.

8. What is a Warp Star?

a) An explosion waiting to happen, contained within
a diamond-like shell.

b) A star that's about to collapse into a black hole.

c) A star that warps the orbit of any planet within reach.

9. What does FOTO stand for?

a) Fear Of Terrible Oranges.

b) Far Orbiting Travel Official.

c) Friends Of The Ood.

10. What is the literal translation of the name 'Vashta Nerada'?

a) The shadows that melt the flesh.

b) The deadly blackness of air.

c) The nightmare shades.

11. What is a squareness gun?

a) A weapon that fires square missiles.

b) A weapon that turns people square.

c) A weapon that punches square-shaped holes through different kinds of matter.

12. What was Project Indigo?

a) An experimental teleport system salvaged from Sontaran technology.

b) A scheme to change the colour of Earth's sky.

c) A manned mission to the planet Indigo.

13. What was the Source, discovered on Messaline?

a) A pool that could heal any wound.

b) A device to transform a planet's ecosystem.

c) Something the Messaline people put on their chips.

14. What was the
Subwave Network?

a) A network of alien
satellites jamming
Earth communications.

b) An undersea military base
with Harriet Jones as
its leader.

c) Sentient software
programmed
to find the
Doctor's allies
on Earth,
operating
on undetectable
frequencies.

15. What is a Cordolaine Signal?

a) A Sontaran invention that expands the bullets in Earth guns, leaving them useless.

b) The Ood call to arms.

c) The way to trigger a Vespiform's mutation.

16. What is an Osterhagen Key designed to do?

a) Help trigger a chain of nuclear explosions that will tear Earth apart.

b) Open an Osterhagen Door.

c) Operate a sonic vibration weapon.

17. CAL is the governing intelligence of the massive computer at the heart of the Library. But what does CAL stand for?

a) Calibrating Automatic Learning.

b) Charlotte Abigail Lux.

c) Computerised Autonomous Librarian.

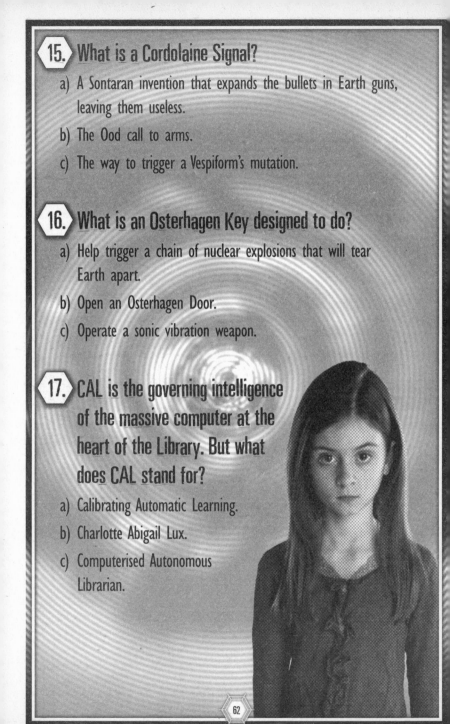

18. What is a Generation 5000 Soldier?

a) A cloned Sontaran warrior.

b) A Pyrovile military construct.

c) A soldier grown from
   a donor's biological tissue.

THE DOCTOR'S DAUGHTER

The Doctor got a whole lot more than he bargained for when he visited the planet Messaline with Donna and Martha – an instant grown-up daughter! How much do you remember about the incredible adventure they shared?

1. On Messaline, the Doctor discovered a machine that could take cells from a body and grow them into another person. *TRUE/FALSE*

2. Jenny was grown from a genetic sample taken from the Doctor's left leg. *TRUE/FALSE*

3. The Doctor hit it off with Jenny immediately. *TRUE/FALSE*

4. A colony of humans had been fighting the alien Hath for one week. *TRUE/FALSE*

5. The humans and Hath had come to Messaline on the same spaceship. *TRUE/FALSE*

6. Donna noticed a string of mysterious numbers printed regularly on the walls of the colony. *TRUE/FALSE*

7. She worked out they were the birthdays of all the human colonists. *TRUE/FALSE*

8. The Doctor and his friends worked out that the humans and Hath had only been at war for one week. *TRUE/FALSE*

9. Jenny hurled herself in front of Martha to save her from being shot. *TRUE/FALSE*

10. Jenny survived and went off to explore the universe by herself. *TRUE/FALSE*

MYSTERIOUS RIDDLE

Here's another mysterious riddle! Each line gives you the clue to a particular letter. If you guess all the right letters and spell them out in order you will get the name of someone who rocked the Doctor's world...

My first is in JUDGE, will the Doctor judge me?

My second's in SOLDIER, that's what I should be,

My third is in GENERATE, also MACHINE,

My fourth's in ANOMALY, that's how I'm seen,

My fifth is in WHY but never in WHO,

Oh, Doctor, admit it —
I grew out of YOU!

RETURN OF THE DALEKS

The Daleks — everyone's favourite murderous machine-creatures — returned from the brink of extinction once again to menace the universe with their most horrifying scheme yet... How much do you remember about these mega-monsters and their hideous plans?

1. Who was the creator of the Daleks?
- a) The Dalek Supreme.
- b) The Chicken Supreme.
- c) Davros.

2. How had he generated a new race of Daleks?
- a) From human skin cells.
- b) From specks of stardust.
- c) From the cells of his own body.

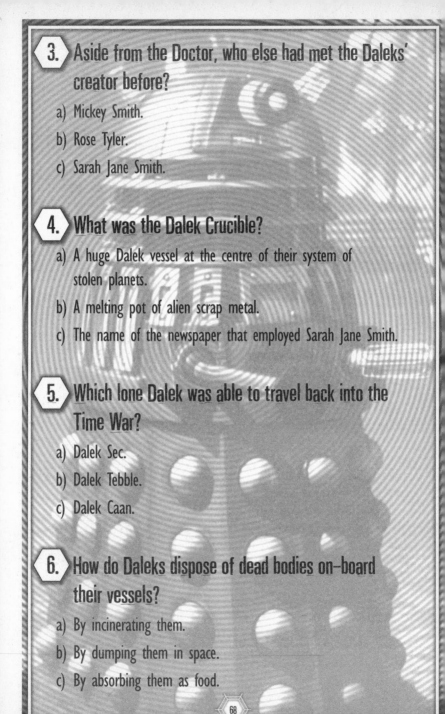

3. Aside from the Doctor, who else had met the Daleks' creator before?

a) Mickey Smith.

b) Rose Tyler.

c) Sarah Jane Smith.

4. What was the Dalek Crucible?

a) A huge Dalek vessel at the centre of their system of stolen planets.

b) A melting pot of alien scrap metal.

c) The name of the newspaper that employed Sarah Jane Smith.

5. Which lone Dalek was able to travel back into the Time War?

a) Dalek Sec.

b) Dalek Tebble.

c) Dalek Caan.

6. How do Daleks dispose of dead bodies on-board their vessels?

a) By incinerating them.

b) By dumping them in space.

c) By absorbing them as food.

ANSWERS:

1. c, 2. c, 3. c, 4. a, 5. c, 6. a, 7. b, 8. a.

SCORES:

7-8   You truly deserve the title of Top Dalek Expert!

4-6   You truly deserve the title of Promising Dalek Student!

0-3   You truly deserve the title of Dalek Dunce — get studying
      at once in case of Dalek invasion!

8. **How were the Daleks ultimately destroyed?**

a) Their power-feeds were overloaded, causing them to explode.

b) They self-destructed.

c) They were crushed by a powerful magnetic wave.

7. **What colour was the Supreme Dalek?**

a) Blue.

b) Red.

c) Silver.

THE UNICORN AND THE WASP

TRUE OR FALSE?

When the Doctor and Donna travelled to the 1920s, they enjoyed a topping time mingling with famous authors, jewel thieves and chasing after a giant insect creature... It was a most unusual murder mystery — but can you remember *Doctor Who-dunnit?* Use your little grey cells and say whether the following statements are true or false...

1. The TARDIS landed in Agatha Christie's house.
   TRUE/FALSE

2. They went to a big party hosted by Professor Peach.
   TRUE/FALSE

3. A famous jewel thief called the Wasp was sneaking about. *TRUE/FALSE*

4. The jewel thief turned into a horrifying insectoid creature called a Vespiform. *TRUE/FALSE*

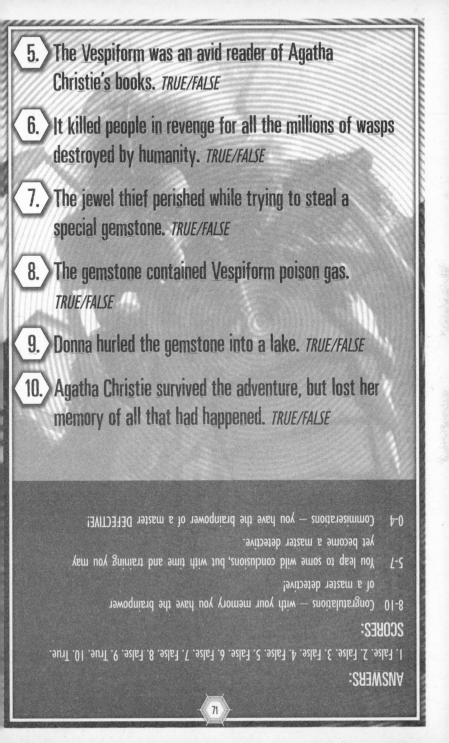

5. The Vespiform was an avid reader of Agatha Christie's books. *TRUE/FALSE*

6. It killed people in revenge for all the millions of wasps destroyed by humanity. *TRUE/FALSE*

7. The jewel thief perished while trying to steal a special gemstone. *TRUE/FALSE*

8. The gemstone contained Vespiform poison gas. *TRUE/FALSE*

9. Donna hurled the gemstone into a lake. *TRUE/FALSE*

10. Agatha Christie survived the adventure, but lost her memory of all that had happened. *TRUE/FALSE*

SCORES:

8-10 Congratulations — with your memory you have the brainpower of a master detective!

5-7 You leap to some wild conclusions, but with time and training you may yet become a master detective.

0-4 Commiserations — you have the brainpower of a master DETECTIVE!

ANSWERS:

1. False. 2. False. 3. False. 4. False. 5. False. 6. False. 7. False. 8. False. 9. True. 10. True.

IDENTITY PARADE

The Doctor's powers of deduction would give one of Agatha Christie's heroes a run for their money. He can identify people, places and objects from only the slimmest of clues. How would you fare? Match each description to one of the things listed below!

1. A handy tool which, when activated, glows blue at the tip.
2. A warm, loud, brave and decisive human female with long red hair.
3. A short, red part-cyborg creature.
4. A withered genius, half-man, half-Dalek.
5. A small golden pendant on a chain, containing alien technology.
6. A stocky, blue-suited war-loving race of clones.

A. Sontarans, B. Davros, C. Adipose signal capsule, D. Bannakaffalatta, E. sonic screwdriver, F. Donna Noble.

SCORES:

5-6 Your razor-sharp mind has cut through this quiz with ease — congratulations!

3-4 Your knife-sharp mind snagged a bit on some of the identifications, but, even so, good going.

0-2 Your totally blunt mind bounced off the questions and landed who knows where — get looking for it!

ANSWERS: 1.E, 2.F, 3.D, 4.B, 5.C, 6.A.

CLOSE COMPANIONS

The Doctor usually enjoys a close friendship with those who travel with him. Recently he was reunited with many old friends — some had changed quite a bit, others had stayed much the same. He even met one from his future! But how close are YOU to the characters whose lives are intertwined with the last of the Time Lords? Take the test and find out!

1. Martha Jones has become a fully qualified:

a) Doctor.

b) Nurse.

c) Lawyer.

2. Sarah Jane Smith has adopted a teenage son named:

a) Doctor.

b) Luke.

c) Zebedee.

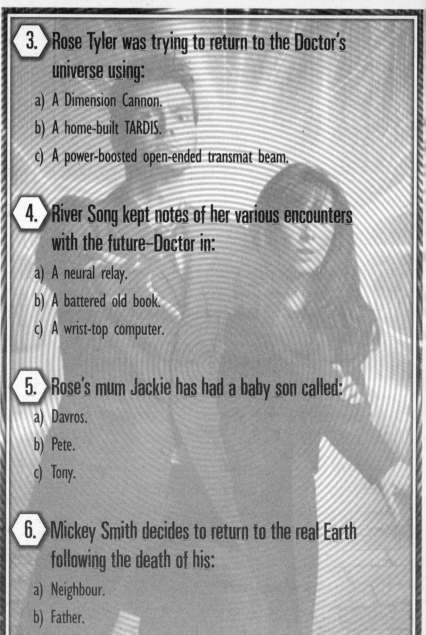

3. Rose Tyler was trying to return to the Doctor's universe using:

a) A Dimension Cannon.

b) A home-built TARDIS.

c) A power-boosted open-ended transmat beam.

4. River Song kept notes of her various encounters with the future-Doctor in:

a) A neural relay.

b) A battered old book.

c) A wrist-top computer.

5. Rose's mum Jackie has had a baby son called:

a) Davros.

b) Pete.

c) Tony.

6. Mickey Smith decides to return to the real Earth following the death of his:

a) Neighbour.

b) Father.

c) Gran.

7. Captain Jack is still in charge of the covert alien-tackling organisation known as:

a) Touchwood.

b) Torchwood.

c) Pyrobranch.

8. Rose remains in her parallel world with:

a) A Dalek.

b) A dog.

c) A part-human version of the Doctor.

SILENCE IN THE LIBRARY

TRUE OR FALSE?

Swarming shadows... sinister spacesuits... a very special person waiting to be met... the Doctor won't forget his experiences in the Library for a long time. But how much have you forgotten?

1. The Library was literally planet-sized. *TRUE/FALSE*

2. It was full of quiet alien scholars browsing the bookshelves. *TRUE/FALSE*

3. Tiny, carnivorous creatures named Vashta Nerada hunted in the shadows of the Library. *TRUE/FALSE*

4. The Doctor was summoned to the Library by an archaeologist called River Song. *TRUE/FALSE*

5. She was leading an expedition of accountants to inspect the Library. *TRUE/FALSE*

6. The entire expedition was eaten alive by monsters.
TRUE/FALSE

7. Donna was taken from the Library into a very different world. *TRUE/FALSE*

8. The Doctor was almost crushed between the pages of a giant book. *TRUE/FALSE*

9. He discovered the mind of a human girl installed at the heart of the Library's computer core.
TRUE/FALSE

10. The Doctor, Donna and River escaped by blowing up the Library. *TRUE/FALSE*

ODD ONE OUT

In each of the sets below, one thing stands out like a rabid, Red-Eyed Ood at a 1920s cocktail party... Sort them out!

1. Mickey, Donna, Wilf, Rose, Martha.

2. The Dalek Crucible, Darillium, Asgard, the Library.

3. Ginger beer, walnuts, chocolate ice cream, anchovies.

4. Anita, Other Dave, Proper Dave, River Song, Miss Evangelista.

5. Germany, New Zealand, China, Alaska, Argentina, Liberia.

6. The Fifteenth Broken Moon of the Medusa Cascade, The Lightning Skies of Cotter Palluni's World, The Diamond Coral Reefs of Kataa Flo Ko, Earth.

ANSWERS:

1. Wilf — the others have all travelled in the TARDIS.

2. The Dalek Crucible — the others are all places where the Doctor has met up with River Song.

3. Chocolate ice cream — the others are all used by the Doctor to drive poison from his body.

4. River Song — the others were devoured by Vashta Nerada.

5. New Zealand — the others are locations of Osterhagen Stations, designed to bring about the self-destruction of Earth.

6. Earth — the others are places the Doctor told Donna he wanted to take her before they parted company.

SCORES:

5-6 A very impressive score in an extremely hard quiz — you can feel proud of yourself!

3-4 Still a pretty impressive result. You show a real aptitude for mind-bending challenges.

0-2 Not a great result — but you are let off. After all, even Luke Rattigan might have puzzled over one or two of these problems!

MIDNIGHT

TRUE OR FALSE?

When the Doctor went on a trip to explore the surface of the planet Midnight, what followed was one of the creepiest, most bizarre adventures of his long, long life. Donna wisely chose not to go, and you too have choices to make — to say whether the statements below are true or false...

1. The planet Midnight was made of solid lead. *TRUE/FALSE*

2. The Doctor travelled with several other people in a kind of space-truck to see an incredible sapphire waterfall. *TRUE/FALSE*

3. The space-truck mysteriously broke down. *TRUE/FALSE*

4. The Doctor glimpsed a band of space monkeys juggling outside on the planet's surface. *TRUE/FALSE*

5. An alien entity managed to possess someone on-board the space truck. *TRUE/FALSE*

6. First it copied everything that the other passengers said. *TRUE/FALSE*

7. Then it started saying things at exactly the same time as the other passengers. *TRUE/FALSE*

8. Finally it started saying the word 'Midnight' over and over. *TRUE/FALSE*

9. Some of the passengers thought the Doctor was possessed by the alien and tried to throw him outside to his death. *TRUE/FALSE*

10. The Doctor freed himself and threw the real alien out onto the planet's surface instead. *TRUE/FALSE*

ANSWERS:

1. False. 2. True. 3. True. 4. False. 5. True. 6. True. 7. True. 8. False. 9. True. 10. False.

SCORES:

8-10 A great score. Like the Hostess on the Midnight expedition, you can take swift, sure action when you need to.

5-7 Not a bad score — but beware of acting like Professor Hobbes, thinking you know it all when really you don't!

0-4 When you read the answers, did you groan and think 'Oh, I KNEW that was the answer really'? If so, you're a bit of a Val Cane — wise after the event!

THE TARDIS TEST

We tend to take the Doctor's incredible ship for granted, but it really is a miracle of time-space exploration. The questions below focus on the TARDIS's involvement in the Doctor's most recent adventures... Good luck!

1. The Doctor reveals that the TARDIS is designed to be flown by how many pilots?

a) One.

b) Twelve.

c) Six.

2. What special method does the Doctor use to open the TARDIS doors when leaving the Library?

a) He rams them with a filing cabinet.

b) He blasts them with a fire extinguisher.

c) He clicks his fingers.

3. Where was the TARDIS discovered in the parallel universe where the Doctor died?

a) Underneath the River Thames.

b) On the Ood-Sphere.

c) In the Medusa Cascade.

4. What happened to the TARDIS when it landed in ancient Pompeii?

a) It was covered in volcanic lava.

b) It was stolen by the Sibylline Sisterhood.

c) It was sold by a sneaky market trader.

5. According to the Doctor, which creatures are experts at fighting TARDISes?

a) Vespiforms.

b) Daleks.

c) The Ood.

6. What interrupted Donna's first lesson in steering the TARDIS?

a) A phone call from Martha Jones.

b) A Dalek hiding behind a pillar.

c) A Hath.

7. Why did the TARDIS suddenly bring the Doctor to the world of Messaline?

a) It needed to refuel.

b) It detected Jenny — but arrived too soon, thus leading to her creation.

c) It detected a world about to be destroyed and wanted to warn the Doctor.

8. How did the Daleks attempt to destroy the TARDIS?

a) By taking down its defences and exposing it to Z-Neutrino energy.

b) By sending 100 Daleks to exterminate it at once.

c) By dropping it into a star.

ANSWERS:

1.c, 2.c, 3.a, 4.c, 5.b, 6.a, 7.b, 8.a.

SCORES:

7-8   Well done — your memory is clearly in full working order.

3-6   Cheer up, memories are like the TARDIS — never completely reliable!

0-2   When the TARDIS rings its cloister bell, it means a wild catastrophe is threatening... such as your brainpower dwindling to a record low!

TURN LEFT

TRUE OR FALSE?

Even the simplest decisions we make can change the world around us, sometimes for good, and sometimes — as Donna discovered — with cataclysmic results. So be warned! Your answers in the quiz below could have more impact than you suspect...

1. On an alien planet, Donna met a fortune-teller. *TRUE/FALSE*

2. The fortune-teller persuaded her to change a single action in her past — to turn right in her car instead of left — so that she never met the Doctor. *TRUE/FALSE*

3. A strange, scuttling creature jumped up on to her head. *TRUE/FALSE*

4. Without Donna to help him, the Doctor died while fighting the Empress of the Racnoss. *TRUE/FALSE*

5. With the Doctor gone, Sarah Jane Smith died while trying to stop the *Titanic* from crashing. *TRUE/FALSE*

6. Martha Jones died trying to stop the Sontarans' destruction of human life. *TRUE/FALSE*

7. Captain Jack persuaded Donna that she had to go back in time and reverse her earlier decision so that she *did* meet the Doctor. *TRUE/FALSE*

8. Donna travelled back in time using a Dalek time machine. *TRUE/FALSE*

9. She had a big raging argument with her other self and persuaded her to turn left instead of right. *TRUE/FALSE*

10. It turned out the creature responsible for trying to change her life was a giant centipede obsessed with Earth history. *TRUE/FALSE*

QUALITY QUOTES

It's time to check your vocabulary banks and try to remember who first said the following memorable words...?

1. 'He saves planets. Rescues civilisations. Defeats terrible creatures. And runs a lot. Seriously, there's an outrageous amount of running involved.'

a) Rose Tyler.

b) A Pyrovile.

c) Donna Noble.

2. 'Molto Bene! Bellissimo! *Allons-y*!'

a) Harriet Jones.

b) The Doctor.

c) The Face of Boe.

3. 'This is too easy! They're running like slimebait from a speelfox!'

a) Commander Skorr.

b) The Dalek Supreme.

c) Agatha Christie.

4. 'The circle must be broken.'

a) Davros.

b) The Ood.

c) Miss Foster.

5. 'When you run with the Doctor it feels like it will never end. But however hard you try, you can't run forever.'

a) Jackie Tyler.

b) Lady Eddison.

c) River Song.

6. 'This is my ultimate victory, Doctor — the destruction of reality itself!'

a) Davros.

b) Halpen.

c) The Doctor.

7. 'Information: You are all going to die.'

a) The Ood.

b) The Host.

c) Agatha Christie.

8. 'I'm the man who is going to save your lives and all six billion people on the planet below. You got a problem with that?'

a) Wilf.

b) The Doctor.

c) Doctor Moon.

SCORES:

7-8   You have a good ear for a memorable line — you must be a great listener!

4-6   Maybe your lugholes need a quick going over with the sonic screwdriver to perk them up a bit.

0-3   Sounds like you don't hang on to much of what you hear... and until you do, you won't know what you're missing!

ANSWERS:

1.c, 2.b, 3.a, 4.b, 5.c, 6.a, 7.b, 8.b.

JOURNEY'S END

The entire Earth snatched out of time and space! The Daleks back, meaner and tougher than ever! The stars going out in each and every universe! Yes, the Doctor faced perhaps the most epic struggle of all his long lives... and if you faced it with him, you should have no trouble saying whether the statements below are true or false!

1. Earth was stolen by the Cybermen. *TRUE/FALSE*

2. The Doctor went to the Shadow Proclamation to try to track it down. *TRUE/FALSE*

3. Meanwhile, Harriet Jones contacted the Doctor's friends and used them to send a signal to the Doctor. *TRUE/FALSE*

4. The TARDIS landed on the moon. *TRUE/FALSE*

5. The Doctor was split into two identical bodies when three Daleks shot him at the same time. *TRUE/FALSE*

6. The Daleks planned to destroy all matter with a Reality Bomb. *TRUE/FALSE*

7. Donna absorbed part of the Doctor's Time Lord powers and became super-brainy. *TRUE/FALSE*

8. She and the two Doctors ruined the Daleks' plans and saved Earth and the stolen planets. *TRUE/FALSE*

9. Donna went off to a space university to make the most of her new mental powers. *TRUE/FALSE*

10. The Doctor continued his travels, all alone once more. *TRUE/FALSE*

ANSWERS:
1. False. 2. True. 3. True. 4. False. 5. False. 6. True. 7. True. 8. True. 9. False. 10. True.

SCORES:

8-10   You hung in there with the Doctor and Donna until the journey's end — and what a wild ride it was!

5-7   You seem to have got a little confused... why not watch the story again and then retake this quiz?

0-4   Most people suffered no side effects when Earth was whizzed through space and back — but it seems to have scrambled your memories something chronic. Don't worry, you'll soon recover — hopefully in time to take the Mega Challenge over the page...

THE MEGA CHALLENGE

This final quiz is designed to test your *Doctor Who* knowledge to the outer limits, so it's longer and tougher than the others in this book. In fact, if you have a Time Lord hand in a bubbling jar close by, now might be a good time to trigger a short term, two-way biological metacrisis and send your brainwaves ballistic! And of course, if you want to make the mega challenge a MEGA, mega challenge, set yourself a three-minute time limit for all 30 questions!

ARE YOU READY?
OH, YES! SO LET'S GO...

1. According to Donna, how long did it take her to master the Dewey Decimal System as used in libraries?

a) Two months.

b) Two days flat.

c) A lifetime.

2. Where can you find a beach with intelligent sand beside a sea of talking fish?

a) Karras Don Kazra Don Slava.

b) Midnight.

c) New Earth.

3. What is the name given to the series of wavelengths used by Migrant Bees as a carrier signal?

a) The Bees' Reprise.

b) The Tandocca Scale.

c) The Buzz of Harmony.

4. How old was the Doctor when he first visited the Medusa Cascade?

a) Five hundred years old.

b) Ninety years old.

c) One million years old.

5. What did Donna notice was unusual about the workforce of the ATMOS central depot?

a) They took no sick days.

b) They were all women.

c) They were all robots.

6. How did River Song prove to the Doctor how close the two of them would become in the future?

a) She revealed that she knew his name.

b) She showed him some of her diary.

c) She kissed him.

7. What did Donna's family call her when she was little?

a) The Troublemaker.

b) Donny.

c) The Little General.

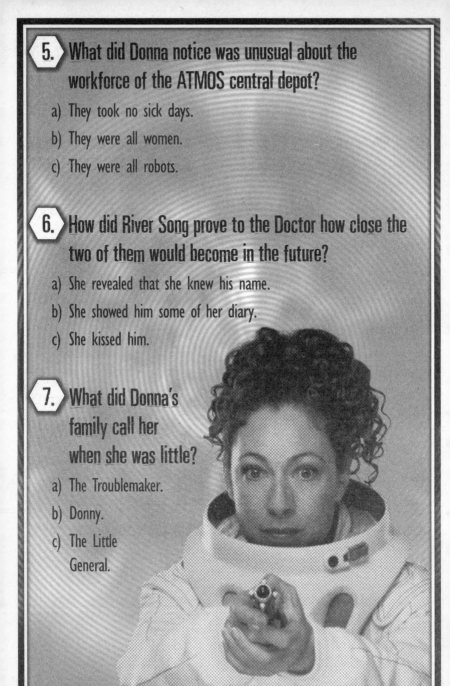

8. What was 'contamination protocol-Z'?

a) Halpen's plan to gas the Ood in their thousands.

b) Staal's plan to alter Earth's atmosphere.

c) The Library's automatic shutdown procedure when under attack.

9. On the planet Midnight, what caused the Crusader 50 to take a detour?

a) An earthquake.

b) A diamondfall at Winter Witch Canyon.

c) Engine trouble.

10. According to the Doctor, what different ways of enjoying books have emerged by the 51st century?

a) Laser etched nanotext pills.

b) Word-spray and type-oil.

c) Fiction mist, holovids and direct-to-brain downloads.

11. Who gave Sarah Jane Smith her Warp Star weapon?

   a) A Dalek.

   b) A Verron Soothsayer.

   c) A Vespiform.

12. 'Jenny' was named by Donna after being inspired by which particular word?

   a) Gender.

   b) Genetics.

   c) Generated.

13. By what nickname was the company Ood Operations sometimes known?

a) Slavery Slapheads.

b) The Double-O.

c) Oody-Ops.

14. If the Sontarans' gas reached 80% density in Earth's atmosphere, what would happen?

a) Humans would start turning into Sontarans.

b) People would start dying.

c) All plant life would wither and die.

15. How does Jenny get past the criss-crossing laser beams blocking her way on Messaline?

a) She performs some incredible gymnastic leaps, twists and turns.

b) She defuses them with a sonic screwdriver.

c) She blasts the arming mechanism with a large gun.

16. What was the name of the ordinary married couple ready to commit a monstrous act on Midnight?

a) Jethro and Dee Dee.

b) Bonnie and Clyde.

c) Biff and Val.

17. Where did Donna once say she learned to whistle?

a) Watching West Ham, every Saturday.

b) By listening to an old kettle.

c) From the Air-Blowers of Vishuti.

18. What level of UNIT security clearance has Martha Jones been given?

a) Security Clearance Four.

b) Security Clearance One.

c) Security Clearance Alpha-one-delta.

19. How long did the Library stay silent before the Lux expedition finally got inside?

a) Five hundred years.

b) Seven days.

c) One hundred years.

20. What was the name of the holiday resort assembled on Midnight?

a) The Leisure Hive.

b) The Leisure Palace.

c) The Dome of Pleasure.

21. For how long has the Sontarans' war with the Rutans been raging?

a) Ten years.

b) Two million years.

c) 50,000 years.

22. Who helped to bring Earth back to its proper place in time and space by transmitting vital information about the TARDIS to Sarah Jane Smith's computer?

a) Donna.

b) K-9.

c) Luke Smith.

23. The 'hair tonic' consumed regularly by Chief Executive Halpen contained what special ingredient?

a) Ood-graft suspended in a biological compound.

b) Poison.

c) The blood of Red-Eyed Ood.

24. In the first year of the Time War, who flew into the jaws of the Nightmare Child aboard their command ship?

a) Davros.

b) The Doctor.

c) Skorr the Sontaran.

25. What protected Gwen and Ianto in Torchwood from the Dalek onslaught?

a) Ten-metre thick steel walls.

b) A giant robot.

c) A Time Lock.

26. When the Pyrovile marble circuit panels were assembled in the correct order, what did they form?

a) An energy converter.

b) A sea-boiler.

c) A heat laser.

27. Whose slogan was 'The Fat Just Walks Away'?

a) ATMOS International.

b) Ood Operations.

c) Adipose Industries.

28. What was the name of Lady Eddison's butler?

a) Greeves.

b) Agatha.

c) Warburton.

29. What kind of engines powered the Crusader 50 on Midnight?

a) Starblaster.

b) Diesel.

c) Micropetrol.

30. What happens on-board the Dalek Crucible when Donna uses the biofeedback shielding to exacerbate the Dalekenium interface, thus inculcating a trip-stitch circuit breaker in the psycho-kinetic threshold manipulator?

a) Nothing.

b) The Daleks lose control of their travel machines.

c) A pit in the floor swallows up Davros.

ANSWERS:

1. b, 2. a, 3. b, 4. b, 5. a, 6. a, 7. c, 8. a, 9. b, 10. c, 11. b, 12. c, 13. b, 14. b, 15. a, 16. c, 17. a, 18. b, 19. c, 20. b, 21. c, 22. b, 23. a, 24. a, 25. c, 26. a, 27. c, 28. a, 29. c, 30. b.

SCORES:

26-30 BELLISSIMO! You are an intergalactic expert in time-space travels. When it comes to brainpower — and to taking the odd lucky guess — you might just give the Doctor himself a run for his money!

22-25 Even a genius like Luke Rattigan would be envious of such a score!

17-21 You're not quite an expert, but your knowledge of the Doctor and his dangerous universe is still above average.

10-16 You enjoy the big picture but you don't have much of an eye for detail. Never mind — so long as you enjoy the ride, that's the main thing!

5-9 A score like this suggests that if somebody said to you, 'Biological metacrisis', you'd probably ask, 'Really? Did the two of them get on?'

0-4 Ouch! You know what you have to do now. Go back to the start of this book and take every quiz again — it might just enhance your Doctor Who knowledge!